W9-CTX-266

WITHDRAWN

BUILDING BLOCKS OF MATH

EXPRESSIONS AND EQUATIONS

Written by Regina Osweiller

Illustrated by Daniel Hawkins

WORLD BOOK

a Scott Fetzer company
Chicago

World Book, Inc.
180 North LaSalle Street
Suite 900
Chicago, Illinois 60601
USA

For information about other World Book publications,
visit our website at www.worldbook.com
or call 1-800-WORLDBK (967-5325).
For information about sales to schools and libraries,
call 1-800-975-3250 (United States),
or 1-800-837-5365 (Canada).

© 2023 World Book, Inc. All rights reserved. This
volume may not be reproduced in whole or in part
in any form without prior written permission from
the publisher.

WORLD BOOK and the GLOBE DEVICE are registered
trademarks or trademarks of World Book, Inc.

Library of Congress Cataloging-in-Publication Data
for this volume has been applied for.

Building Blocks of Math
ISBN: 978-0-7166-4253-4 (set, hc.)

Expressions and Equations
ISBN: 978-0-7166-4256-5 (hc.)

Also available as:
ISBN: 978-0-7166-4266-4 (e-book)

Printed in India by Thomson Press (India) Limited,
Uttar Pradesh, India
2nd printing June 2023

WORLD BOOK STAFF
Executive Committee
President: Geoff Broderick
Vice President, Editorial: Tom Evans
Vice President, Finance: Donald D. Keller
Vice President, Marketing: Jean Lin
Vice President, International: Eddy Kisman
Vice President, Technology: Jason Dole
Director, Human Resources: Bev Ecker

Editorial
Manager, New Content: Jeff De La Rosa
Associate Manager, New Product:
  Nicholas Kilzer
Sr. Editor: William M. Harrod
Proofreader: Nathalie Strassheim

Graphics and Design
Sr. Visual Communications Designer:
  Melanie Bender
Sr. Web Designer/Digital Media Developer:
  Matt Carrington

Acknowledgments:
Writer: Regina Osweiller
Illustrator: Daniel Hawkins/The Bright Agency
Colorist: Leo Trinidad/The Bright Agency
Series Advisor: Marjorie Frank
Special thanks to KnowledgeWorks Global Ltd.

TABLE OF CONTENTS

Does "2k" mean "2 times k?"

$5 + 2k$

Yes! Both expressions mean "2 times k." Usually, we write expressions without a times symbol, such as x or a dot.

We also use fractions instead of the "divided by" sign. Instead of 3 ÷ 4, we write $\frac{3}{4}$.

C'mon, Times Sign. They don't need us today!

The **terms** of an expression are the parts that are added and subtracted.

Notice that a term can have any combination of numbers and variables—so long as they're being multiplied or divided, and not added or subtracted.

Math Expression	Number of Terms
1. $7x$	1
2. $x + 7$	2
3. $x^2 - 7$	2
4. $7^2 + 7x - \frac{1}{x}$	3

A. 7 more than x

B. 7 times x

C. 7 squared plus 7 times x, minus 1 divided by x

D. 7 less than x squared

T 4-G4

Beep-beep, whirrrrr, beep!*

*Translation: Match the word expressions with the math expressions in the table. Use your own paper.

See page 40 for answers.

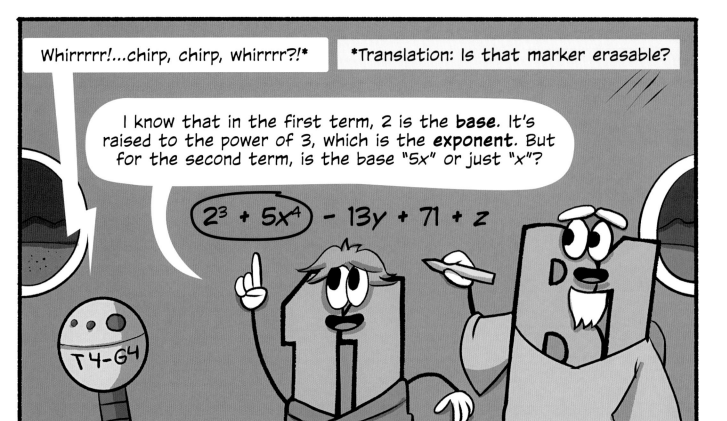

Whirrrrr!...chirp, chirp, whirrrr?!*

*Translation: Is that marker erasable?

I know that in the first term, 2 is the **base**. It's raised to the power of 3, which is the **exponent**. But for the second term, is the base "5x" or just "x"?

$$2^3 + 5x^4 - 13y + 71 + z$$

T4-G4

Yes, sometimes the base is an unknown number, or variable. For $5x^4$, the base is the variable x, and not 5 times x. The number 4 is the exponent, so x is raised to the fourth power.

$+ 71 + z$

The **coefficients** of an expression are the number factors that multiply the variables.

A **constant** is a term in an expression that contains numbers only, with no variables. The value of a constant won't change.

Q6-LU

Old
Numb
Varia
Coeff
Const
Expon

When a variable has no number factor to its left, the coefficient is understood to be 1.

$$2^3 + 5x^4 - 13y + 71 + z$$

Old B1's Expression:
Number of terms: 5
Variables: x, y, z
Coefficients: 5, 13, 1
Constants: 2^3 and 71
Exponents: 3 and 4

On a separate sheet of paper, identify the terms, variables, coefficients, exponents, and constants for these expressions.

1. $8b^2 - 3b + 17$

2. $\frac{2}{3} + m + 5n - 11$

3. $12w - x^3 - 6$

See page 40 for answers.

EVALUATE EXPRESSIONS

MENU	Space dollars
BLUE MILK	10
ORANGE JUICE	8
APPLE JUICE	7
LEMONADE	4
WATER	2

Distance to Planet Basketball (parsecs)

$8 + 1.5 + 3 - 0.5$, which equals 12

Fee for a Journey to Planet Basketball (space dollars)

$200 + a$

(Ask your pilot what a means.)

When an expression has only numbers, it has one possible value only.

How can I find the value of this expression?

EXIT

I can tell you all about evaluating expressions with variables, kid.

Sven Zero! The legendary pilot of the spaceship *Infinite Spitfire*!

Gwooorrf!*

*Also the legendary co-pilot, Hairy Eight!

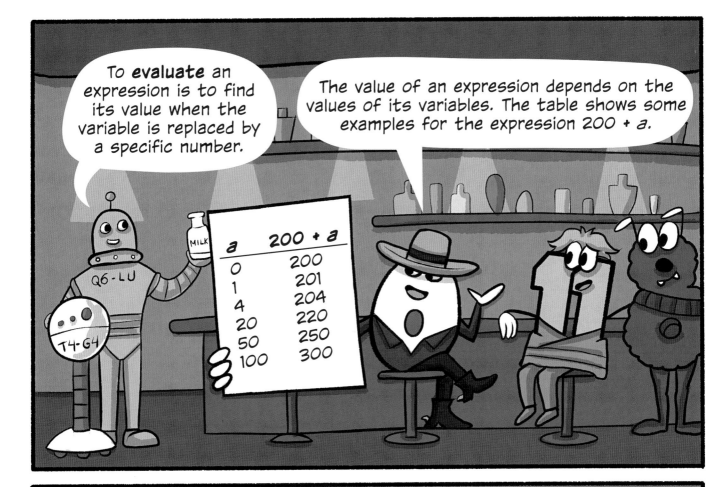

The expression:	$2(6 + 9) - 5^2$	
P: Parentheses	$2\,(\mathbf{15}) - 5^2$	Solve anything within the parentheses.
E: Exponent	$2(15) - \mathbf{25}$	Evaluate the value of the exponential number.
MD: Multiplication and Division	$\mathbf{30} - 25$	Do any multiplication or division.
AS: Addition and Subtraction	$\mathbf{5}$	Do any addition or subtraction.

The letters in PEMDAS show the order of operations for simplifying a mathematical expression. First is "P" for parentheses.

So you want 5 tickets! That's 70 space dollars per ticket, plus an 18-space-dollar service charge.

$5(70) + 18$
$= 350 + 18$
$= 368$

Use PEMDAS to simplify these expressions. Write on your own paper.

1. $8(9 - 4) + 2^2$

2. $(3 + 5)^2 - (4 - 3)^3$

3. $\dfrac{3}{4} + 5^2 - 4(5)$

See page 40 for answers.

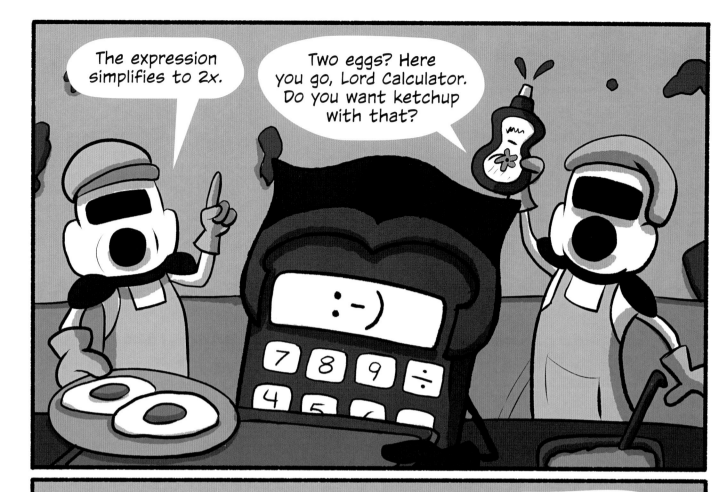

An expression and its simplified version are examples of **equivalent expressions**, meaning they equal each other at any values of their variables.

On a separate sheet of paper, write simplified, equivalent expressions for these examples.

Remember, the first step is to identify the like terms!

1. $8 + 6x + 2x - 4$
2. $2x^2 + 5 - x^2 + 1 - x^2$
3. $4 + 4x + 4y + 3x - 3y$
4. $8a - 2b + 9a - b - 3$

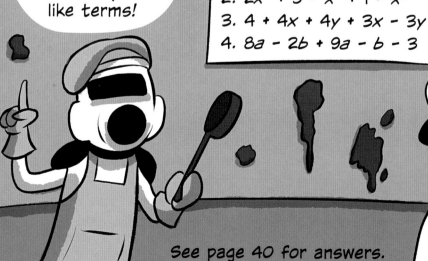

See page 40 for answers.

17

SOLVE ONE-VARIABLE EQUATIONS

Now aboard the *Infinite Spitfire*, Fluke Eleven is practicing the skills he needs to solve more math problems and rescue the princess.

So here we have our first equation. An **equation** is a math sentence with an equal sign. The expressions on either side of the equal sign have the same value.

How do I solve this equation?

$$n + 9 = 11$$

First, put down the baguette and take off the blindfold!

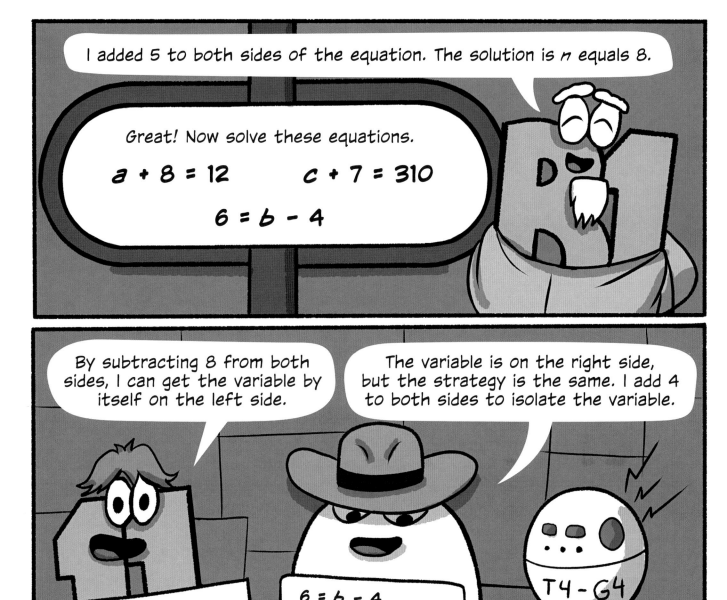

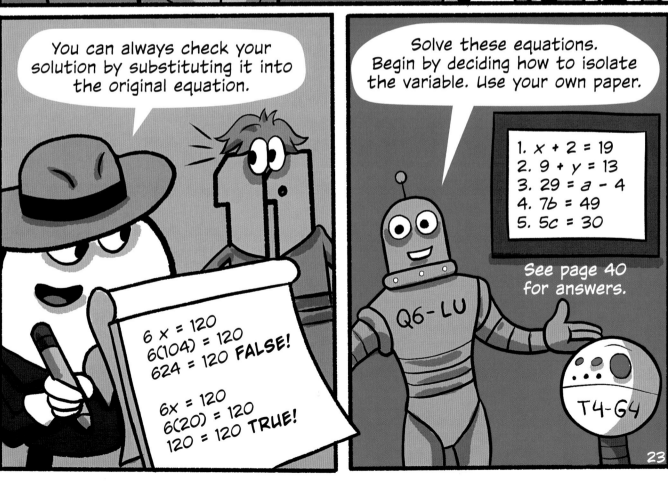

23

See page 40 for answers.

25

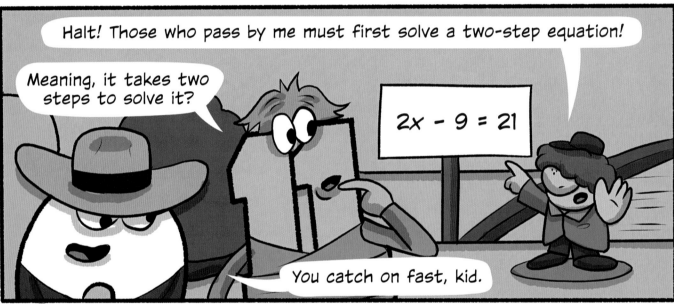

Say, Calc, how many alligators do we have on this space station?

$4x^2 = 400$

Oh, I see x is squared! First I'll divide both sides by 4.

$$\frac{4x^2}{4} = \frac{400}{4}$$

$$x^2 = 100$$

I know of only one positive number that has the square of 100, and that's 10. So you have 10 alligators.

Grrowlff. Grr-Shrpof! Jd67?*

*Solve these two-step problems. For the first three problems, the first step is named for you. Remember PEMDAS! Use your own paper.

1. $5n + 11 = 31$ — Subtract 11 from both sides.
2. $41 = 2j - 7$ — Add 7 to both sides.
3. $a - 8^2 = 1$ — Evaluate 8^2.
4. $3b - 5 = 22$
5. $2^3 = 4x$

See page 40 for answers.

$3(x - 5) = 18$

Divide both sides by 3.

$$\frac{3(x - 5)}{3} = \frac{18}{3}$$

Simplify.

$x - 5 = 6$

Add 5 to both sides.

$x = 11$

$3(x - 5) = 18$

Apply the distributive property.

$3x - 15 = 1$

Add 15 to both sides.

$3x = 33$

Divide each side by 3.

$x = 11$

The **distributive property** tells how to solve expressions in the form of $a(b + c)$ or $a(b - c)$.

We first multiply each number inside the parentheses by the number outside the parentheses. Then we do the addition or subtraction.

The solution is x equals 11.

MATH

My, what a ridiculous bunch of equations we're making!

Stop complaining, and start solving!

CHOMP!

$$\frac{x}{9} = 10$$

Multiply both sides of the equation by 9.

$$9\left(\frac{x}{9}\right) = 9(10)$$

$$x = 90$$

BONK!

$$3(x+5) = 4x$$

Remove parentheses with the distributive property.

$$3x + 15 = 4x$$

Subtract 3x from both sides.

$$3x + 15 - 3x = 4x - 3x$$

Combine like terms.

$$15 = x$$

Remember PEMDAS
Parentheses
Exponents
Multiply/Divide
Add/Subtract

BIFF

$3(x + 8) - 2x = 27 + 2^4$

Remove parentheses with the distributive property.

$3x + 24 - 2x = 27 + 2^4$

Evaluate the expression with the exponent.

$3x - 2x + 24 = 27 + 16$

Combine the like terms.

$x + 24 = 43$

Subtract 24 from both sides.

$x = 19$

The steps for solving an equation with many terms are the same steps we already practiced. We just have to repeat the steps.

SPACE DOCK

I see that my baguette is 9 centimeters longer than yours, and together their length is 83 centimeters. So how long is each baguette?

Let x represent the shorter baguette, so x + 9 is the longer one. The sum of the two expressions is 83.

$x + (x + 9) = 83$
$2x + 9 = 83$
Subtract 9 from both sides.
$2x = 74$
Divide both sides by 2.
$x = 37$

The short baguette is 37 centimeters, and the longer one is 37 + 9, or 46 centimeters.

I have 300 points in my frequent flyer account, and I get 25 points for every alligator I bring back home.

How many alligators do I need to end up with for a total of 450 points?

I can find out! Let n be the number of alligators, so $25n$ is the number of points they're worth.

The expression $300 + 25n$ is the total number of points, which must equal 450.

You need 6 alligators.

$$300 + 25n = 450$$
Subtract 300 from both sides.
$$25n = 150$$
Divide by 25.
$$n = 6$$

My goodness, he speaks English!

To solve word problems, look for ways to change the words into an equation.

The first step is to assign a variable to the unknown quantity, such as the length of a baguette or the number of alligators.

Then write the equation that shows the relationship.

BEEP! ZRRRT

T4-G4

Q6-LU

SHOW WHAT YOU KNOW

1. Evaluate each of these expressions when x = 3.

A. 2x + 5
B. x² – 2
C. 4(x + 2)
D. 5x + 210

2. Use PEMDAS to simplify each expression.

A. 4(5 + 2) – 2³
B. (6 + 3)² – (9 – 7)²
C. 4² + 2(6 – 4) – 8

3. Grwolfe Shs-jogcww.*

*Translation: Solve each of these multistep equations for d.

A. $5(d + 2) = 10d$

B. $d + 5^2 = 37$

C. $3(d - 2) + 4d = 15 + 7$

---

4. **Multiple choice.**
Use substitution to solve each equation.

1. Which value of m solves the equation $2m + 5 = 19$?
   A. m = 3
   B. m = 5
   C. m = 7

2. Which value of h solves the equation $15 - 3h = 9$?
   A. h = 2
   B. h = 4
   C. h = 6

3. Which value of b solves the equation $b + 4b = 7b - 8$?
   A. b = 2
   B. b = 3
   C. b = 4

4. Which value of d solves the equation $d + 12 = 3^2 + 2d$?
   A. m = 3
   B. m = 5
   C. m = 7

See page 40 for answers.

ANSWERS

Page 7:
1. B, 2. A, 3. D, 4. C

Page 9:
1. Terms: $8b^2$, 3b, and 17
   Variable: b
   Coefficients: 8 and 3
   Exponent: 2
   Constant: 17

2. Terms: $\frac{2}{3}$, m, 5n, and 11
   Variable: m and n
   Coefficients: 1 and 5
   Exponents: none
   Constant: $\frac{2}{3}$ and 11

3. Terms: 12w, x^3, and 6
   Variables: w and x
   Coefficients: 12 and 1
   Exponent: 3
   Constant: 6

Page 13:
1. 6, 12, 24
2. 1, 13, 61
3. 5, 15, 35
4. 16, 22, 34

Page 15:
1. 44
2. 63
3. $5\frac{3}{4}$

Page 17
1. 8x + 4
2. 6
3. 7x + y + 4
4. 17a − 3b − 3

Page 19
1. n = 3
2. n = 2
3. n = 3
4. n = 1

Page 23:
1. x = 17
2. y = 4
3. a = 33
4. b = 7
5. c = 6

Page 25:
1. x = 8
2. x = 16
3. x = 9
4. x = 15

Page 27:
1. n = 4
2. j = 24
3. a = 65
4. b = 9
5. x = 2

SHOW WHAT YOU KNOW
Pages 38-39:

1. A. 11 - First, multiply 2 and 3 to get 6.
      Then, add 6 and 5 to get 11.

   B. 7 - First, square 3 to get 9.
      Then, subtract 2 from 9 to get 7.

   C. 20 - First, add 3 and 2 to get 5.
      Then, multiply 4 and 5 to get 20.

   D. 225 - First, 5 and 3 to get 15.
      Then, add 15 and 210 to get 225.

2. A. 20 - Parentheses: $4(7) - 2^3$
         Exponents: 4(7) − 8
         Multiplication: 28 − 8
         Subtraction: 20

   B. 77 - Parentheses: $(9)^2 - (2)^2$
         Exponent: 81 − 4
         Subtraction: 77

   C. 12 - Parentheses: $4^2 + 2(2) - 8$
         Exponent: 16 + 2(2) − 8
         Multiplication: 16 + 4 − 8
         Addition/Subtraction: 12

3. A. 2 - Remove the parentheses with the
      distributive property:
      5d + 10 = 10d
      Subtract 5d from both sides:
      10 = 5d
      Divide both sides by 5: 2 = d

   B. 12 - Evaluate the expression with the
      exponent: d + 25 = 37
      Subtract 25 from both sides:
      d = 12

   C. 4 - Remove the parentheses with
      the distributive property:
      3d − 6 + 4d = 15 + 7
      Combine the like terms:
      7d − 6 = 22
      Add 6 to both sides: 7d = 28
      Divide both sides by 7: d = 4

4. 1. The equation is solved when m = 7 (C).
   2. The equation is solved when h = 2 (A).
   3. The equation is solved when b = 4 (C).
   4. The equation is solved when d = 3 (B).

CONTRA COSTA COUNTY LIBRARY

3 1901 10021 1798